COMICAL COLIN
by TONY GARTH

Colin loved to play practical jokes on people.

He would fill his dad's shoes with custard.

He would put salt in the sugar bowl.

He would even fill his mum and dad's bed with marbles.

Colin thought that his jokes were hilarious, but his mum and dad didn't.

One day, Colin's mum had invited the vicar round for tea. What she didn't know was that Colin had put his giant, deluxe, whoopee cushion on the armchair.

"Sit down vicar," said Colin's mum, "Would you care for some tea?"

The vicar sat down.

PTHWAAAAARP!! Went the whoopee cushion.

The vicar was very embarrassed, and so was Colin's mum.

Colin, on the other hand was in fits of laughter.

"Hiya dad!" said Colin one evening when his dad came home from work. "Shake hands?"

Colin's dad held out his hand.

ZZZZAAPPP!!

"Argh!" said Colin's dad, "I've been zapped!"

"Ha ha ha," laughed Colin, "It's my new super duper hand buzzer. Do you like it?"

"Not much, no," grumbled Colin's dad.

"Mum?" said Colin.

"Yes dear."

"You know how you're really scared of spiders?"

"Y-yes dear."

"Well there's a huge hairy one on the table."

"Aaargh!" screamed Colin's mum as she ran out of the kitchen."

"Ha ha ha!" laughed Colin as he picked up the giant spider, "It's only made of plastic."

"That was funny, wasn't it mum... mum?"

The following morning, Colin heard his dad go into the bathroom.

"Are you having a shower dad?" he shouted through the door.

"That's right Colin," replied his dad.

"Well be sure to use that new, special bar of soap that I've left for you."

"Oh, right. Thanks Colin," said his dad.

Colin waited.

"Argh! Help! I've gone blue!" shouted Colin's dad.

"Ha ha ha!" laughed Colin, "It's joke soap. It makes your skin go blue when you wash with it."

Colin's dad was not amused, he had a blue face for three days.

"Ouch! Oooh! Ouch!" shouted Colin as he ran into the house.

"Ouch! Look mum, I've got a big nail stuck in my finger!"

Colin's mum turned a strange shade of green.

"Oh my goodness!" she shouted. "Quick! We'd better get you to hospital straight away."

"Ha ha ha!" laughed Colin as he took off the nail, "It's only pretend, see. You should have seen your face."

Colin's mum didn't think it was at all funny.

"Here, dad?" said Colin one morning, "Do you want to look through my new telescope before you go to work?"

"Oh yes, thanks," said his dad and put the telescope to his eye.

Colin began to giggle.

"What's so funny?" asked his dad as he put the telescope down. He didn't know that it was a trick telescope that left a black ring around his eye.

"Oh, nothing dad," said Colin as his dad left for work.

Colin's dad wondered why everyone in the office that day was laughing at him.

That evening when Colin was tucked up in bed, Colin's mum and dad sat down in front of the TV to watch a scary film about ghosts.

"This film is very scary," said Colin's mum after a while."

"Yes, it is." agreed his dad.

Just then the door burst open and there stood... a GHOST!

"Woooo!" it said.

Colin's mum and dad nearly jumped out of their socks.

Ha ha ha!" laughed Colin, "That scared you. It's only me wearing an old sheet on my head.

Colin's mum and dad were too shaken to speak.

"I've just about had enough of Colin's silly jokes," said Colin's dad when Colin had gone back to bed, "We'll have to do something about it."

Colin's mum agreed and they sat down to think of a plan.

Two days later, a parcel arrived with Colin's name on it.

"Wow! A parcel, for me!" exclaimed Colin, "I wonder what it is?"

"You'd better open it." said his dad with a sly smile.

Colin began to untie the string and suddenly the parcel burst open and out popped a horrible, scary monster!

"Argh!" screamed Colin, "A scary monster! Let me out."

Colin ran as fast as he could and out of the back door... Straight into his blow-up paddling pool which was full of horrible, green, slimy goo.

"Ha ha ha!" laughed Colin's dad, "Now that's what I call a practical joke."

"You should have seen your face," giggled Colin's mum.

"I hate practical jokes," muttered Colin, "they're just not funny!"

CALL OUR LITTLE MONSTERS INFO LINE FOR LOTS MORE: 0906 216 0066

Calls cost 25p per minute.